2. Skipping Song

Dialogue, by mischievous students

Off we go, one, two, three, four, Now, is the car-riage at the door? Off we go, four, five six, sev-en Did you say the riv-er Sev-ern? Off we go, five, six, sev-en eight, Shall we cross the Me-nai Strait? Off we go, six, sev-en eight nine Sail-ing down the riv-er Tyne. Off we go, sev-en eight, nine, ten. To a pret-ty Scot-tish glen._____ Is there room for me in-side? Hur-ry up! Where is the guide? On your bike, or in your car, You'll be go-ing ver-y far. If a train will suit you fine, You'll be rush-ing down the line. Do you want to take a plane Just to go to Am-ster--dam? I think you are quite in-sane, You could get there in a train!_____

3. Reading Lesson

Spelling Song, by obedient students

Calme
1st verse

Zo - e, your ze - bra Zonks in al - ge - bra, Zig - zags to Som-er-set,

Zips on the clar-i-net.   A zeal-ous Zu - lu In Hon-o-lu-lu, Rides on a zith-er,

Hith - er and thith - er.   A za - ny liz - ard, Caught in a bliz - zard,

Saw a big zom - bie, In Ab - er-crom-bie.   Zinc and zir-co-ni-um

On a eu-pho-ni-um Bring out the gus-to, Make them cry bra-vo. Bra-vo!

4. The Luck of the Draw

Song, by mischievous students

Animé *1st verse*

Plong!   Ding dong ding dong ding   click!   What was that?   It was a

stick.   Since when do sticks go click?   O - ho!   You're a dunce and out you go!

5. Miss Spectacles

Round, by mischievous students

6. Mea Culpa

Song, by obedient students

7. The Monitor Alexander

Round, by mischievous students

8. Deserved Praise

Song, by obedient students

Animé

1st verse

What a pleas-ure it is to be top of the class, So well be-haved, quick off the mark, Al-ways do-ing our best and a-chiev-ing a pass, It's al-ways us teach-ers re-mark. Al-ways pay-ing at-ten-tion and do-ing our best, We're nev-er gig-gling, nev-er smirk-ing. And we keep ver-y clean, we're im-pec-ca-bly dressed, We're ver-y se-rious when we're work-ing.

2nd verse

Nev-er chat-ting or lark-ing a-bout in the class We fin-ish all our ex-er-cis-es. Ev-er reach-ing a lev-el we want to sur-pass, That's how we win so man-y priz-es. La-ter on if we have our own kids we shall say: If you can do as well as we did, It's a-gree-a-ble go-ing to school ev-'ry day, En-cour-age-ments are hard-ly need-ed.

9. The Argument

Dialogue, by all students*

Quadrille-Polka

You're no good in the class! You'll nev-er get a pass! You're sil - ly as can be! You're jeal-ous I can see! A load of lit - tle swots, Who spoil our fun and games! And you're a bunch of clots, For call - ing us those names! We'll tear your books in two, And fill your pens with glue, What a hul - la - ba - loo! We'll tell the teach-er all, You'll both - er us no more, He will give you what for! You think you're ver - y bright, Be - cause your marks are good. You hav-en't un-der - stood, You're just a trog - lo - dyte! You'll see when you leave school, Un - worth-y par - a - site! You say that out of spite, You sil - ly, lit - tle fool!

TOGETHER

You sil - ly, lit - tle fool! _____
You're just a trog - lo - dyte! _____

* M. : *mischievous students*
  O. : *obedient students*

10. The Orchestra of the Obedient Students

by obedient students

Hear the vi - o - lin, the cel - lo, Vi - o - la and dou - ble bass.

Ah, the sound is smooth and mel - low, El - e - gant and full of grace!

These won - der - ful in - stru - ments Give to all the great - est pleas - ure.

They mer - it our com - pli - ments, Like the pia - no, for good meas - ure.

Next, the flute and clar - i - net, The French horn and the trom - bone, With the tu - ba

and the trum - pet, Al - so have a pret - ty tone. Ah, you on - ly have to

prac - tice Then you'll en - rap - ture the ear, And you will ad - mit the fact is

Hard work is not so aus - tere. And e - ven the tim - pa - ni, Or the bass drum and the

gong, Will gen - er - ate eu - pho - ny. If you're skilled, you can't go wrong.

11. The Orchestra of the Mischievous Students

by mischievous students

Tango *1st verse*
What a pain,___ the vi - o - lin! The pi - an - o is - n't

ea - sy, And a drum will make you quea - sy Till you take some med - i - cine.

As for the flute and the o - boe, Or e - ven the clar - i - net We nei - ther care nor re - gret

2nd verse
They're all as dead as the do - do. What a bore___ is the trom - bone, And the

tu - ba is a dan - ger. We can think of noth - ing strang - er Or more apt to make us groan.

Why should we scratch a gui - tar? It's un - plea - sant to the ear Why do they want us to hear

3rd verse
Sounds that we find so bi - zarre? It is all too com - pli - cat - ed, With a walk - man it's much

bet - ter Both for jazz and op - er - et - ta. How much more so - phis - ti - cat - ed!

Why should we spend so much time Learn - ing ru - di - ments of mu - sic? Prac - tic - ing scales make us too sick.

It's not a joy, it's a crime, In that all you have to know Is how to lis - ten with plea - sure.

Then, when you've had a full meas - ure, You will cry "bra - vis - si - mo!".

12. Final Chorus: In Praise of Computers

by all students

9 790044 080724